Disney VILLAINS

HADES

THE HORN OF PLENTY

AUTUMN
PUBLISHING

AUTUMN
PUBLISHING

Published in 2023
First published in the UK by Autumn Publishing
An imprint of Igloo Books Ltd
Cottage Farm, NN6 0BJ, UK
Owned by Bonnier Books
Sveavägen 56, Stockholm, Sweden
www.igloobooks.com

Story by Manlio Castagna and Harriet Webster
for Book on a Tree, London

Art by Lorenzo Colangeli (comic pencils),
Francesca Dell'Omodarme (comic paints)
for Book on a Tree, London

Cover by Lorenzo Colangeli (pencils),
Francesca Dell'Omodarme (paints)

Historical and cultural background supervision by
IW Group, Los Angeles – New York – San Francisco

Lettering by Studio RAM, Bologna

Cover and design by Falcinelli & Co., Roma

0623 001
2 4 6 8 10 9 7 5 3 1
ISBN 978-1-83771-341-7

Printed and manufactured in China

Disney VILLAINS

HADES

THE HORN OF PLENTY

CASTAGNA ✦ WEBSTER ✦ COLANGELI ✦ DELL'OMODARME

WORDBOX

The Horn of Plenty: The Cornucopia or 'Horn of Plenty' symbolises abundance in folklore and is often depicted in painting and sculpture as a curved goat's horn overflowing with fruit.

Dodekatheon: The Dodekatheon labels the group of twelve Olympian Gods: Apollo, Aphrodite, Ares, Athena, Artemis, Demeter, Hephaestus, Hera, Hermes, Hestia, Poseidon and Zeus.

The Gigantomachy: This is the name of the great battle between the Gods and the Giants, or *Gigantes*. Although the Giants were defeated, some believed they remained under mountains and were responsible for volcanic eruptions and other geothermal activities.

Thread of Life Tapestry: In Greek mythology, every mortal's destiny is woven into the tapestry of life soon after their birth. The three Fates are responsible for it: Clotho would spin the thread, Lachesis would measure it and Atropos would then cut it, ending the mortal's life.

The River Styx: Styx is one of the rivers separating the land of the living from the land of the dead. To cross over it to reach the underworld, a dead person would need to be transported on Charon's boat.

THE GODS ARE GETTING READY FOR THE FEAST DAY OF THE DODEKATHEON, A CELEBRATION FOR THE GODS OF MOUNT OLYMPUS...

HAPPY FEAST DAY!

UH-OH. HADES IS GETTING READY, TOO!

I'LL RUIN THEIR RIDICULOUS PARTY!

I'LL MAKE THEM REGRET NOT INVITING ME **AGAIN** THIS YEAR!

MEANWHILE, SOME GODS ARE SETTING THE MOOD UP IN THE SKY...

... DEEP DOWN IN THE SEA...

♪ LALALALA LALA

... AND ON LAND!

HMM. IT'S A LITTLE DARK TONIGHT.

... OTHERS ARE MAKING FINISHING TOUCHES...

FLICK

FWOOSH

... AND STILL OTHERS MUST START AGAIN.

SORRY, HESTIA!

HUFFF.

THE MUSES GET THE SHOW STARTED...

WHOA!

CRASH

WATCH OUT!

BANG

HUH?! WHERE DID SHE GO?

APHRODITE IS ALWAYS FLAWLESS!

AH, THERE SHE IS!

CLAP CLAP CLAP CLAP CLAP

... THERE'S A LITTLE VIP ABOUT TO MAKE HER ENTRANCE!

MEHH!

AWWWWWWW!

THAT'S NOT THE ONLY SURPRISE OF THE NIGHT...

BOOO

BOOO

HADES?! THIS YEAR, TOO?

HEY, I COME IN PEACE!

I SEE HOW IT IS.

GRRR!

IT WOULD BE BETTER IF YOU LET ME PASS, YOU MIMING GODS!

HADES, MY LITTLE BROTHER, IT'S NOT THAT WE DON'T WANT YOU HERE, BUT YOU KNOW HOW IT IS...

FOR ONCE WE'D LIKE TO GET TO THE END OF A PARTY WITHOUT HAVING TO REBUILD ALL OF OLYMPUS!

AND PLUS, WITHOUT YOU, THE UNDERWORLD IS SUCH A MORGUE!

AMALTHEA AND ZEUS GREW UP TOGETHER.

MEEEH!

THE GOAT NOURISHED ZEUS WITH HER MILK TO MAKE HIM BIG AND STRONG.

BUT ONE DAY, AS YOUNG ZEUS WAS PLAYING WITH AMALTHEA, AN ACCIDENT OCCURRED...

AMALTHEA'S HORN BROKE.

TO MAKE UP FOR IT, AND AS A SIGN OF GRATITUDE, ZEUS BLESSED THE BROKEN HORN AND REATTACHED IT...

... SO THAT THE HORN'S OWNER WOULD GAIN **EVERYTHING** THEY DESIRED.

CLOSE YOUR EYES AND THINK OF EARTH...

THE HUMANS PRAY TO DEMETER TO ENSURE THERE WILL BE A BOUNTIFUL HARVEST...

UNTIL THEY DON'T.

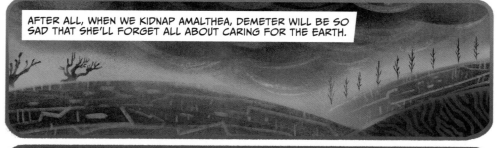

AFTER ALL, WHEN WE KIDNAP AMALTHEA, DEMETER WILL BE SO SAD THAT SHE'LL FORGET ALL ABOUT CARING FOR THE EARTH.

AND WITH NO FOOD TO EAT, IT'S ONLY A MATTER OF TIME BEFORE THE HUMANS STOP PRAYING TO ALL THE GODS...

WITH THE GODS WEAK WITHOUT THE STRENGTH OF HUMAN PRAYERS, WE WILL BE CALLING UPON THE SUPPORT OF SOME OTHER EARTH DWELLERS...

PORPHYRION AND HIS 23 FELLOW GIANT BUDDIES WILL HELP US OVERTHROW ZEUS AND HIS SNOTTY OLYMPIANS ONCE AND FOR ALL!

COUGH.

YES, WHAT IS IT?!

EXCUSE ME, YOUR MOST LUGUBRIOUSNESS, BUT DIDN'T THE GIANTS TRY THIS ALREADY? THE GIGANTOMACHY, OR WHATEVER THEY CALLED IT?

TEN SECONDS LATER...

ZZZZZ

NOM, NOM!

TEN MORE SECONDS...

THUD
THUD
THUD
THUD
THUD

THAT WAS EASY!

YEAH, JUST ONE MORE MOUTH TO FEED!

AMALTHEA...

WELL, WHAT ARE YOU TWO WAITING FOR?! LET'S GET HER OUT.

THAT'S IT...

OwWW!

BSSH!

MEHP!

OOPS.

DON'T JUST STAND THERE, GO AFTER HER!

UM, HADES?

YEAH?!

WELL, YOU KNOW HOW YOU SAID, "I DON'T WANT TO BE THE KING OF THIS SQUALID UNDERWORLD ANYMORE"?

UH-HUH...

WELL, YOU **WERE** HOLDING AMALTHEA'S MAGIC HORN AT THE SAME TIME...

... SO, UM, THAT WAS TECHNICALLY A WISH.

HUFF.

ZEUS! I HAVE NEWS FROM THE UNDERWORLD!

GOOD NEWS, I HOPE!

AMALTHEA IS THERE!

HADES? I SHOULD HAVE KNOWN.

DEMETER?!

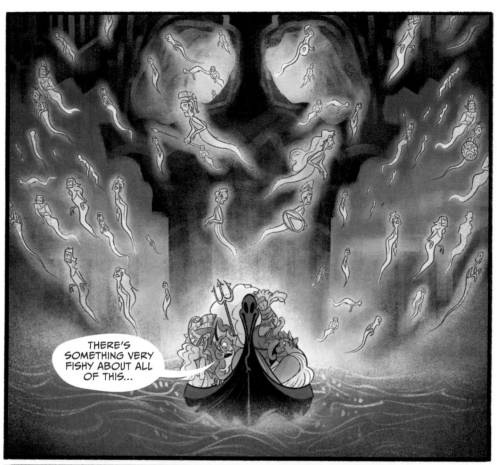

BACK ON MOUNT OLYMPUS...

CRACK

URGH, WHERE AM I?